G·L·U·E

*A Leadership Development Strategy
to Bond and Unite*

BY AMY P. KELLY

G.L.U.E.: A Leadership Development Strategy to Bond and Unite

Trilogy Christian Publishers
A Wholly Owned Subsidiary of Trinity Broadcasting Network
2442 Michelle Drive, Tustin, CA 92780

Trilogy Christian Publishing/TBN and colophon are trademarks of Trinity Broadcasting Network. For information about special discounts for bulk purchases, please contact Trilogy Christian Publishing.

Trilogy Disclaimer: The views and content expressed in this book are those of the author and may not necessarily reflect the views and doctrine of Trilogy Christian Publishing or the Trinity Broadcasting Network.

Manufactured in the United States of America
10 9 8 7 6 5 4 3 2 1
Library of Congress Cataloging-in-Publication Data is available.

ISBN: 978-1-63769-736-8
E-ISBN: 978-1-63769-737-5

Dedication for G.L.U.E.

This book is dedicated to God.
Thank you for the answer to unity in this world.

This book is dedicated to Jon and Kathryn Gordon
and the entire Jon Gordon team,
who formed a stronger bond during the pandemic
through the unity of God's love.
This book is dedicated to *you!*

For any time,
you might not have known how to apply G.L.U.E.
There is still time to unite and build a bond.

"And over all these virtues put on love, which binds
them all together in perfect unity."
— Colossians 3:14

Praise for G.L.U.E.

"Amy P. Kelly has done a masterful job creating a compelling story of personal development and relationship restoration that will impact many lives. The lessons in *G.L.U.E.* are invaluable to take life or work relationships that need repair and heal them to create a stronger bond. This is a must-read for any leader's ability to bond and unite relationships and teams. After all, God's Love Unites Everyone."

—Tami Matheny
Mental Game Coach and
Author of *This Is Good* and *The Confident Athlete*

"This is a story that will help people navigate difficult situations in life and work relationships. When there is disagreement, relationships do not have to break. When we love and support others, they feel safe to grow, and we grow at the same time. That is what leadership development is all about, supporting others' growth and the inevitable self-growth that occurs in the process."

—Julie Nee
Vice President of Training,
The Jon Gordon Companies

"*G.L.U.E.* is a great story for leaders in families, businesses, schools, or churches all over the world. All readers will gain a new perspective on grace, humility, and leading."

—Thomas Williams
Former NFL Player, Author, and Consultant

"*G.L.U.E.* is a timely story that has the power to speak to each of us. In a world that has led us to believe that broken things are to be discarded and rarely revisited, *G.L.U.E.* reminds us that broken things do not need to remain broken. Amy has done a masterful job of illustrating that division, even deep division, has the power to be repaired and restored with the right mindset."

—Melissa Johnson
CEO of Oh My Cupcakes, Author, and Speaker

"*G.L.U.E.* is a well-written piece and quite relatable to everyone, weaving in the ebbs and flows of everyday life as we deal with the interconnectivity of our personal lives, business, and faith. Amy's depiction of how we wrestle with our emotions is brought to life, as we cater to the needs and demands of those around us, especially those we work with. While we balance the wins, expectations, hurt, and disappointments, no matter where we are or who we are interacting with, we find that—with God's love present—we can rise above the challenges and foster an environment where grace abounds."

—Saina Shagaya-Osifadé
Wife, Mother of four, and Senior Market Insights Manager,
Corp Communications and Marketing

Acknowledgments

Thank you to my family:
Jim, Natalie, Patrick, Daniel, and Samuel Kelly.
We are on a mission to share G.L.U.E.

"I have given them the glory that you gave me, that they may be as one as we are one—I in them and you in me—so that they may be brought to complete unity. Then the world will know that you sent me and have loved them even as you have loved me."
— John 17:22–23

G.L.U.E.

Glue can be applied to build things
and form a strong bond.
Glue repairs things and holds things together
after they have been broken or split apart.

Table of Contents

Foreword

I started working with Amy after she created a learning and development program at her company that featured my book *The Energy Bus*. The program was so effective that I asked her to help me create a resource to help other individuals, teams, and organizations utilize the principles and practices from the book to achieve exceptional results. We wrote *The Energy Bus Field Guide* together, and that project launched a partnership to continue developing exceptional leaders, teams, and organizational cultures.

Five years later, Amy leads our *Power of a Positive Team* consulting practice and speaks, trains, coaches, and consults with leaders and their teams all over the world. I have personally watched her conduct workshops, facilitate training, coach executives, and design leadership development programs that help leaders improve their leadership and build stronger teams.

While Amy and I share a love of leadership, culture, and teamwork, what truly binds us together is our faith and love of Jesus. We believe God's love is the most powerful force in the world. We believe the Holy Spirit is the best coach, trainer, and advocate and that God's Word instructs and guides us through any situation in life.

Amy and I spoke at the beginning of the pandemic about what God was saying to us about how to serve effectively during a time when the world was reeling, people were scared and confused, and all our speaking events, training classes, and consulting projects were getting canceled or put on hold. We knew we wanted to keep helping individuals, teams, and organizations, especially through such a tough time. We both knew we would keep going, and we both knew we would seek God for His guidance on what to do next.

I told Amy that I was going to find a way to keep doing the work and driving the mission and asked her for ideas about what she thought our team should do. I still remember what Amy said to me, "God told me to obey. I am going to seek Him with all my heart and do what He tells me."

The next thing I knew, Amy was volunteering to lead book clubs on *The Power of a Positive Team* and some of my other books. She began hosting weekly prayer calls for our Jon Gordon team. She started doing pro-bono talks while we prepared to launch more virtual offerings to support our clients.

We both learned a great deal during the pandemic, and when Amy told me about G.L.U.E. and how she believed it would help individuals, teams, families, companies, and communities, I knew it would be a powerful tool for people to learn, grow, heal, and unite.

When you read G.L.U.E., you will learn about the single most effective personal development strategy of all time. The book teaches a process to build stronger bonds in personal and business relationships, repair broken personal and business relationships, and help people grow personally and professionally.

After Amy wrote G.L.U.E. and told me about it, she called me a few weeks later very excited about something she found. She said, "Look at the beginning of chapter 6 in *The Power of a Positive Team*. Read the first paragraph. There is confirmation G.L.U.E. fits perfectly into the plan for the work we do."

"Positivity is the glue in the process of building a powerful team, but to truly be a great team, you need to do more than just be positive. You need to communicate, connect, commit, and care to create meaningful relationships, strong bonds, and team unity" (*The Power of a Positive Team*, 79).

After you read this book, you will never think about glue the same way, and your life and work will be better for it.

—Jon Gordon
Author of *The Power of Positive Leadership*,
The Power of a Positive Team, and *The Energy Bus*

Author's Message to You

When you read this book, you might think, "Is this a story about leadership?" The answer is yes. I believe that you are the leader of your life. The way you make decisions and the way you manage your work and life relationships are your life's leadership. God has given us the power and free will to make choices and decisions as we lead in our life. He has given us the directions for our fullest life possible in His Word, and the way we move through our life is the story of our leadership development journey.

The reason I decided to share G.L.U.E. is to serve you. This story came through the opportunities in my life and work to observe the impact of successful and unsuccessful relationship management in people's leadership development. I wanted to share what I have learned as a human resources executive, executive coach, leadership development professional, and entrepreneur. I want you to get stronger and more effective in your own life's leadership skills through learning about G.L.U.E.

The power to maintain unity when so many forces work against that goal is fertile ground for leadership and life development. What a leadership competency! It is one that many executives ask me to identify as people get evaluated for hire and promotion in teams and organizations. Leaders are needed that keep teams and organizations together in the toughest times. Leaders are needed to keep peace and find common ground, not jump into the pool of division and strife. These relationship management skills are where the good work is done to grow leadership effectiveness.

If you can restore a relationship through reading this book, if you can recalibrate and reconcile a relationship inside yourself through reading this book, if you can prepare for work and life relationship challenges through reading this book, then the work of this book is a success, and you have grown as a leader.

I have seen screaming matches in offices due to breaks in work relationships, and I have seen the impact on the teams and communities when business relationships break. The people in these scenarios take all that stress and anxiety home, and then it impacts their families and ripples out to impact everyone around them. When leaders are equipped to respond differently in their life and work, we find the blessing of unity and strong bonds. Those strong, united relationships create an environment—really a culture—for personal and professional abundance as we act as the leaders of our lives. We have the power to unite and create strong bonds as we follow the one who provided the answer. The answer is provided in the Bible, and this story of G.L.U.E. is one illustration of how to bring those fruits to the leadership story of your life. With each stronger relationship, you move one step forward in the goal of unity through Christ in our world. Let's bond and unite!

Chapter One

The Award

"How good and pleasant it is when God's people
live together in unity!"

— Psalm 133:1

Linda and Cindy were on stage. The lights were bright, and the business partners were standing side by side smiling as they accepted the award for Small Business of the Year. The two friends had worked on their store, The Hope Chest, for many years, and it was finally paying off. The Hope Chest started to turn a profit consistently a few years back, and Linda and Cindy were excited about the impact in the community and finally in their business bank account.

Linda and Cindy opened The Hope Chest to provide unique gifts to customers who wanted to give meaningful presents for the milestones and special moments in people's lives. Milestones like birthdays, graduations, engagements, weddings, anniversaries, new babies, adoptions, new homes, baptisms, new jobs, and retirements. Gifts for any time that people came together to celebrate something special. Or gifts to share in the joys of everyday life. Gifts to honor friendship, provide encouragement, demonstrate love, and give hope.

The women believed people needed encouragement, hope, and love to live their best life, and Linda and Cindy built their business on hope and hard work for their mission. They worked together with the belief that The Hope Chest would deliver the best gift options for their clients' important moments in life. They wanted to give people encouragement and hope and the power to spread it through thoughtful and perfectly timed gifts. They also believed the business would become a way to support a positive environment in their community, as well as a bright future for their own families.

Standing next to each other on stage and accepting the award for Small Business of the Year seemed like confirmation of the importance of their mission and the start of even brighter days ahead. Linda looked over at Cindy and smiled. She was savoring every moment with her treasured friend. She loved Cindy, and they had been through so much together to get to this point. So many highs and lows. So much laughter and some tears. Their families and many other business owners in the community were present to celebrate this milestone in the growth of their business and the sacrifices made to get there. They were all happy with what Linda and Cindy built and were eager to enjoy the moment with them. It was a phenomenal night filled with smiles, hugs, and applause. The business partners were grateful for all they had accomplished through The Hope Chest. They had no idea how their friendship was about to be tested.

Chapter Two

Breaking Apart

"When my heart was grieved and my spirit embittered, I was senseless and ignorant; I was a brute beast before you."

— Psalm 73:21–22

Two weeks after the award ceremony, Linda came into the store and found a post-it note on her computer screen in Cindy's writing. The pair loved to use bright sticky notes with inspirational sayings to leave reminders for each other. They sold this type of product in their store, and they would surprise each other by ordering new styles and quotes without the other knowing. It was a tradition to leave notes on each other's desk with a new product the other believed would fit with The Hope Chest mission while also using the notes to encourage each other and live their purpose to celebrate life's important milestones and simple moments through meaningful gifts.

The post-it note Linda found on her computer screen was a plain one. It did not have an inspirational saying or a unique design. It was a generic shade of yellow and said, "Come find me when you get in, please."

The note was a little more abrupt than usual. It lacked the fun and colorful design of Cindy's normal notes, but Linda shrugged it off and walked to the front of the store. She found Cindy organizing a bright, multi-color set of new coffee mugs on one of the display tables. When Linda walked up, Cindy smiled and turned to Janice at the register and said, "Can you please watch the front on your own for a couple of minutes?" Janice replied that she was fine, and Cindy asked Linda if they could talk in the back office. This was fine with Linda, and the pair walked down the hall behind the register to their shared office in the back of the store.

On the way to their office, Linda started to get a funny feeling in the pit of her stomach. She was not sure why it was happening, but she felt something different in the energy with Cindy and was anxious to find out what it was.

When they got to their office, Cindy closed the door and asked Linda to sit down. Linda sat at her desk, and Cindy sat down, too. The atmosphere was starting to feel very strange to Linda. Cindy said, "It has been amazing building The Hope Chest together and serving this community. I am very grateful for all we have done. However, I wanted to let you know I have decided to follow my dream to open a gift store on the other side of town with a focus on jewelry. You know my love for jewelry, and I feel it is the right time to step out on my own to build on the success here and follow that dream through my own store. You are really the heart of The Hope Chest, and I am more of a behind-the-scenes person, so not much will change. You can continue to do the things you love and find someone else to do the administrative tasks. I will open the new store and work on the strategy and the operations of the business."

Linda was listening and trying to understand what Cindy was saying. She was not sure what was happening. Cindy was saying things that she had never heard before, and it was surprising to hear her say it in such a matter-of-fact tone. Cindy looked very serious, but Linda did not know if she was saying she wanted to expand and open a new store together or if she wanted to split her time between The Hope Chest and another store. It sounded like she wanted to walk away and take the great ideas from The Hope Chest and do her own thing. It sounded like she did not want to be a part of what they built together with The Hope Chest any longer.

Linda said, "Are you looking to expand, or do you want to hire more staff so you can split your time between two businesses?"

Cindy replied, "No. I believe I've learned all I can here, and we've used so many of our great ideas. The Hope Chest can stand on its own, especially with you at the helm leading the vision and strategy. It is time for us to do things separately, and I wanted to see if you would buy out my portion of the business so that I can move on and fulfill my dream to specialize in jewelry. I can use many of the same approaches we created to serve customers and give them an opportunity to purchase jewelry for the important times in their lives. I've wanted to specialize in this for a long time, and this is the right time to move forward."

Linda looked at Cindy. Cindy looked directly back at Linda. Linda was not sure how to feel, and she still did not understand what was happening. It felt awkward and strange, and something else was building inside her, too, but she was not able to identify it fully yet. Lately, it had seemed like Cindy was a bit distant, but Linda thought it was her style to be a bit more reserved, so she tried to give her friend space to do things in the way she was comfortable. She remembered Cindy talking about adding a line of jewelry at one time, but it had never come up again. She did not remember a time when Cindy said it was her dream to work with jewelry. Linda would have supported adding jewelry to their product offering. She was so confused.

Was Cindy really saying that she wanted to leave and open a new store? Was she really acting as if she could just walk out with all their ideas for a specialty gift store and do her own thing? Why would she want to do that? How could she believe it was okay to walk away and leave everything and everyone behind?

The Hope Chest was originally Linda's idea, and Cindy could not just change the words around and try to open a specialty gift shop that would compete against their original business.

Linda tried to breathe, but deep inside, she felt her heart and muscles tightening. Heat ran up her neck. She could feel her heart beating quickly, and it felt like her heartbeat was accelerating to the point where it would come out of her chest. Linda instinctively raised her hand to her chest, intending to slow her heart down.

Linda focused on breathing slowly and managed to regain some of her ability to communicate with Cindy. She said, "Can we talk more about this later today? I have so many questions, and I need time to think." Linda was grateful she managed to stay calm as she spoke, but the frustration, and hurt, and anger were building inside. *Who did Cindy think she was? Why would she do this and think it was okay to take their business ideas for a gift store and use them on her own new business? Why did she feel betrayed?* All that was running through Linda's mind was, *Why would she do this? Why would she want to leave? Why would she betray me?*

Cindy responded to Linda's question by saying, "Sure. I can talk around 7 p.m. after we close the store. It will have to be no more than thirty minutes, though, because I signed a lease for the new store and have a meeting across town with the landlord." She continued, "I know this isn't easy, but I promise you, everything will be okay, and it will work out great for everyone. This is what is best for me, and I hope you can understand and support me. You know I've wanted to focus on jewelry for a while now."

Linda did not say anything because she was still too caught off guard and working to understand what was happening while maintaining her composure. Cindy said she would see Linda later that evening and left.

Chapter Three

Splintered in Pieces

"Do nothing out of selfish ambition or vain conceit.
Rather, in humility value others above yourselves,
not looking to your own interests but each of you to
the interests of the others."

— Philippians 2:3–4

Linda sat and stared at the wall after Cindy walked out of the office. Then she picked up her car keys and wrote on a plain yellow post-it note, "I'll be back at 7 p.m." She put the plain, sad-looking note on Cindy's computer screen and walked out the door.

When Linda got home, she walked past her husband and children in the family room and went into her office. She had not realized it, but tears were running down her face, and her body felt tired and heavy.

At that moment, she saw the Small Business of the Year award sitting on the top shelf of her bookcase. It was next to a small wooden chest that Cindy had given her when they opened the store. It was supposed to represent the name of the store, The Hope Chest, and all the hopes they had for what they would do together and how they would help others. Before she knew it, Linda picked up the business award and threw it across the room. It hit the wall and fell on the floor. *That felt good*, she thought. She decided to continue in her anger because it made her feel better in the moment. Next, she picked up the small replica of a hope chest Cindy had given her and threw it on the floor. The chest cracked, and small pieces of wood flew across the room. She looked over at the business award. It had a crack in the clear plastic base. *Perfect*, Linda thought. *Now, I do not have to look at the reminders of someone who would take my ideas and leave me behind like I meant nothing to her and act like it was all no big deal. If she wanted to break our partnership and friendship apart, this is a good start.*

Chapter Four

People Watching

"I appeal to you, brothers and sisters, in the name of our Lord Jesus Christ, that all of you agree with one another in what you say and that there be no divisions among you, but that you be perfectly united in mind and thought."

— 1 Corinthians 1:10

Linda heard a knock on her office door. She said, "Come in." It was Justin, her youngest son. He asked her, "Are you okay, Mom?"

Linda took a deep breath and started to pick up the pieces of the mini hope chest and the cracked award.

Justin started helping her and said, "What happened? I heard some thuds. Did you break those?"

Linda put the award and the pieces of the mini hope chest on the corner of her desk. She turned around and faced Justin.

"I got frustrated with someone that took something at the store. I should not have thrown things. I let my emotions take over for a minute. Do not worry. Everything is fine, and I will take care of it," Linda said. "It is good to see you. Is there anything you need?"

Justin looked at his mom. She did not look okay. She looked sad and tired. He said, "I can ask you later. It was nothing."

"No," Linda said. "What is it?"

"Can Peter come to church with us tomorrow morning?" Justin asked. "His dad is out of town, and his mom has to work, so I thought he could come with us and then come over for lunch."

Linda did not really want to have one more thing to deal with in the morning, but she knew that Justin really wanted to build this friendship. *Plus, Peter is a fantastic boy, and Justin and Peter should not have to suffer just because I'm tired and frustrated*, Linda thought.

"Sure," she said to Justin. "Just make sure he will be ready at 8 a.m. when we go by to pick him up."

"Thank you, Mom. I really appreciate it," Justin said. "I know Peter will, too."

Chapter Five

The Text

"A person with good sense is patient, and it is to his credit that he overlooks an offense."

— Proverbs 19:11, (GW)

"In your anger do not sin. Do not let the sun go down while you are still angry"

— Ephesians 4:26

Linda was sitting in the back office at The Hope Chest at 7 p.m., waiting for Cindy. The shop was closed, and she sat looking at the piles of paperwork and mail. At 7:10 p.m., Linda got a text from Cindy. It said, "I'm sorry. My new landlord asked me to come earlier. Can we please talk later this week?"

Linda wanted to scream. She could not believe how inconsiderate Cindy was to take their business model, move forward with a new store, and not show up for their discussion while Linda made a special trip back to the store to wait for her.

Linda clicked the thumbs up option on the text from Cindy and grabbed her purse and keys. *I'm out of here*, she thought. *I need to start dealing with reality. Cindy is breaking up our partnership, taking our business ideas, and doing her own thing. I cannot imagine what she is thinking. I must forget about her, put her in the past, and move on. And, for sure, I will not help her. She will regret she left, and I will make sure everyone knows that she betrayed me and stole the idea for a specialty gift shop. I came up with that years ago, and she has a lot of nerve to leave and use the same concept. And, on top of it, to act like it is not a big deal. Well, I will show her.*

Linda felt like her emotions were getting the best of her, but she felt justified in her anger toward Cindy. She got in the car and continued to fume all the way home. Her thoughts kept stoking the fire of anger inside her mind.

Later, when she sat in the family room with her family, she was distracted. Her thoughts were divided, and she was not paying attention to her family as they watched their favorite Saturday night cooking show. Her mind was focused on negative thoughts about the woman she thought was one of her best friends. She kept thinking and thinking about it. The more she focused on how hurt she felt, the angrier she became. Linda thought this was an unforgivable betrayal. Her feelings of frustration and anger got bigger and bigger. It was like she could feel every negative emotion slicing at her insides and creating wounds to her heart.

The family watched the show, cleaned up the kitchen together, and went to bed. Linda was there with them, but she was not really there. She was still thinking about all the reasons she would never speak to Cindy again, and the pain in her chest and stomach continued.

She robotically said good night to her husband Paul and went to bed angry.

Chapter Six

The Mirror

"When they kept on questioning him, he straightened up and said to them, 'Let any one of you who is without sin be the first to throw a stone at her.'"

— John 8:7

Linda woke up and began to make coffee. She could hear everyone starting to move around upstairs. Paul had taken the dog for a walk. They had forty-five minutes before they needed to leave to pick up Peter for church.

Linda checked her phone. No new messages from Cindy. She was not surprised, but she kept hoping Cindy would reach out and say she changed her mind, or say she was sorry, or say why she would want to leave, or just say something to admit that what she was doing was not right. Linda could not stop thinking about it, and while she continued to ponder all the reasons she was disappointed in Cindy, she heard gurgling water. The sound started to get louder.

Linda turned around and saw the coffee pot overflowing. Linda had put too much water in the machine, and she had been careless putting in the coffee grounds. She was distracted, and it was causing her to miss things. The coffee pot was just one impact of a divided and distracted mind.

Look at the mess I've created just with the coffee. I'm creating messes because I am not able to stop thinking of my anger.

It was true. The pot was filled with coffee now, and it had chunks of grounds visible throughout the pot. The pot sat in a puddle of overflow that was sizzling on the coffee pot burner, and the smell was not good. Linda unplugged the coffee machine and started to clean up the mess. She did not want to waste precious time cleaning up messes that never had to happen in the first place. She knew she needed to slow down and get her focus back.

Linda started to think about church, and as she was wiping the counter, she said a prayer that the message today would help her. She knew she needed to stop thinking about the problems with Cindy and the future of The Hope Chest. She was filled with anger and judgment, and she was letting it have a hold on her mind.

After cleaning up the rest of the mess and finishing getting ready for church, everyone in the family hurried out the door to the car. She hurried behind them. As she passed the hall mirror, Linda caught a glimpse of herself. She did not like what she saw. A hard face looked back at her, and she blamed Cindy.

Chapter Seven

The Decision: Anger or Trust

"If it is possible, as far as it depends on you, live at peace with everyone."

— Romans 12:18

"Do not be wise in your own eyes; fear the Lord and turn away from evil."

— Proverbs 3:7

Linda held Paul's hand as they walked into church. After they checked in, Justin and his friend Peter sprinted into their class. Linda's other children said, "Mom, I hope you feel better," and walked off toward the middle school and high school rooms.

Linda thought, *Cindy is the one that is betraying me. Why do I feel so miserable? How can everyone tell something is wrong with me?*

Her thoughts jumped quickly to the angry woman she saw in the mirror when leaving the house that morning. All the pain and frustration were evident on her face. She was wearing her anger and hurt on the inside and the outside.

How do I get rid of this horrible feeling? she thought. *I am losing a friend. She is taking my idea for our business, and I am not even sure what will happen to The Hope Chest without two owners caring for it. This is not fair, and I do not want to see her again, but I must talk to her to sort out details and figure out a plan. I feel like I am drowning in all these feelings and am overwhelmed by every aspect of the situation. I also feel ridiculous by continuing to let this control my thoughts.* Frustration built on frustration. In her mind, she was crying out for help and exhausted while continuing to focus on the negative. She continued to think about all the reasons Cindy might do this, and all of them were bad. Linda's anger continued to build. *There is no justifiable reason for her to do this to me,* she thought.

Just then, the music started to play, and Paul squeezed her hand when they stood up to start singing. Linda was still thinking of Cindy, and she did not want to sing.

After the songs were finished, the pastor began his message. He was talking about forgiveness. He mentioned Mark 11:25, "And when you stand praying, if you hold anything against anyone, forgive them, so that your Father in heaven may forgive you your sins." Linda did not want to hear it. She did not want to forgive Cindy. She tuned out most of the message. She did hear the pastor mention the gift of grace. He was saying that justice is giving someone what they deserve. Mercy is not giving someone what they deserve, and grace is being given what we do not deserve. Jesus provided all of us grace and forgiveness of our sins through his death on the cross.

Linda had heard that before, and she believed it, but today she did not want to hear it. She wanted to focus on herself and her own hurts and anger. She wanted to keep forgiveness for herself, but she did not want it for Cindy. And, more importantly, she did not want to give anything to Cindy. She wanted Cindy to get what she deserved for betraying her, for leaving, for taking the idea that was originally hers, and for springing it on her and acting like it was no big deal. The thoughts kept swirling around and around in her head. She was not sure how much more she could take. She feared what she would do the next time she had to see Cindy. Cindy deserved the silent treatment. They would never talk again.

Yes! Linda thought. *That is what I will do. I will never look at her or talk to her again. I will freeze her out. She will pay for betraying me. I will make sure I tell everyone what she did, and her new store will fail before it ever opens.*

Linda decided she had the perfect plan, but she still felt horrible. The anger and frustration continued to eat at her from the inside. The thoughts she was having did not even feel like her, but she just kept allowing them to come into her mind and keep her focused on the anger and pain. She was not giving any space in her heart or thoughts to what Cindy might be going through. She continued to focus on herself and act based on her feelings. She was starting to realize acting on her feelings was not a wise thing to do, but she got distracted by movement at the front of the room and let that thought pass.

At that moment, everyone started reading. The pastor put something up on the screen. The whole room was reading Proverbs 3:5–6 except her. They were saying, "Trust in the LORD with all your heart and lean not on your own understanding; in all your ways submit to him, and he will make your paths straight."

Amid her anger and frustration, Linda felt a pull on her heart. The pull got a little stronger, and while the pull on her heart increased, she noticed a shift. She stopped thinking about how mad she was at Cindy. She still wanted Cindy to suffer like she was suffering, but she felt something changing. She knew it was not healthy or right to center her thoughts on anger and frustration day and night. She needed to stop focusing on herself, but she was having trouble breaking the negative pattern of her thoughts. Linda realized how selfish she was being but did not know what to do next. She knew that most of what she was upset about she had not even talked to Cindy about yet. She needed to center herself on something stable and give Cindy a chance to share her side of the situation.

It had been a short time since Cindy told her about the new store, and she was letting her feelings and emotions affect her focus, sleep, and family. At that moment, she made a decision to trust that God would take care of everything. She made the decision a little bit ahead of her feelings, and she was trusting that her feelings would catch up to her decision. She had to put her trust in something other than the smothering negativity, anger, and self-centered thinking that was strangling her from the inside out. She tried to open a little space in her heart and mind to consider Cindy and what might be going on from her side of the situation. Linda decided to think of someone other than herself. She also decided to believe the best of her friend. She decided to be a friend to Cindy because she wanted her friend to be happy. It was not easy, but she kept thinking, *I've got to try and trust something other than myself because I am lost on how to deal with this on my own. I will stop putting my trust in what I can do and put my trust in His capabilities and promises. I will center myself in God's Word and prayer, not my feelings and negative emotions.*

It seemed almost ridiculous to trust an invisible force to help her with such a massive problem. She believed in God, but if she was honest in her current mindset, she did not feel confident this would work. The key was trust.

However, Linda knew she could not continue to go down the path she was on because her anger was building toward a future blow-up. She realized that she did not handle it well when people moved on to something new. This was an important and somewhat exciting revelation. She remembered other times in the past where she had a strong reaction to people leaving her team or moving on to something new. When one of The Hope Chest's sales coordinators left for a sales manager role at another store, Linda took it personally and was unkind when the employee left. She realized she had focused on herself in that situation, too.

She knew negative behavior and resentment would hurt people she cared about, and it would also hurt her health. She did not want to hurt her family, her customers, her employees, and her community. She needed to grow beyond this type of response. If her family, team, and community saw The Hope Chest break into a million pieces, it would hurt them. She did not know if this would work, but she knew that being angry all the time was going to bring more destruction, and she really cared about Cindy and both their families. It was worth a try to look at the situation from a new perspective. She knew thinking only about her side of the situation was selfish, and she was starting to realize it was because she was hurt and afraid. And, it was because she was telling herself a story about what Cindy was doing and why she was doing it. She did not even know all the facts yet. All she had were reactions and emotions. She was not behaving like the leader and friend she intended to be. She was letting her emotions and negative thoughts take the lead. It was almost like the negative thoughts were building barriers in her mind blocking productive thoughts and highlighting the negative options as the only way. She needed to trust in the God she knew could do anything and follow Him. By following Him, she knew through the power of the Holy Spirit inside her she could be the leader she was created to be.

The verse was still up on the screen as the pastor kept talking. She said it quietly to herself, "I will trust in the Lord with all my heart. I will not lean on my own understanding of the circumstances. I will obey God and submit to what He tells me. I trust that He will work this out so that I can move forward in peace, and so can Cindy."

She started feeling a little bit better and a little bit better after she said it. She started to feel a sense of peace and the barriers in her mind breaking down. She did not know how it was happening. The improvement in the pain in her stomach was unexplainable but undeniable. She appreciated it and was willing to keep trusting to have that continue. Now she had to have a conversation with Cindy and see if this was really going to make a difference. She knew she needed a bit more time to prepare and was grateful Cindy had moved their original meeting. A little time to slow down, to think, and breathe was starting to make a difference. She felt the urge to pray more, and she would pray for Cindy, too. She knew that it was better to be a peacemaker, and she was willing to make the decision to do that. She made the decision to trust.

Chapter Eight

Too Many Examples

"Be kind to one another, tenderhearted, forgiving one another, as God in Christ forgave you."

— Ephesians 4:32

Linda, her family, and Justin's friend Peter sat down for Sunday lunch after church. They were having tacos, and everyone was passing the toppings around the table when the examples started.

First, Justin and Peter shared a story about their friend Darren. They told everyone that Darren had been on their youth football team but decided to leave and start his own team. The league required that you have a certain number of members, and Darren put together the numbers to have a new team. Justin told the table, "Darren is making his team blue and red, too, just like ours. He is calling his team the tigers, and we are the lions. He is such a copycat. He stole our colors, and he betrayed us by starting a new team. Peter and I are going to ignore him at school, and Mom, can you text his mom and make sure to get my water bottle back? I let him borrow it a few weeks ago, and I do not want him to have it anymore."

Linda looked at her husband, Paul, and then she turned to Justin. "Honey, Darren is allowed to start his own team and come up with his own ideas. He followed the rules, and anyone

G·L·U·E

can have a mascot like a lion or a tiger and the colors red and blue. You do not own that set of colors or animal mascots. You should support Darren and think about what is best for him, not just your own plans. You do not know why he started his own team, and he may be choosing the name and colors because he thinks so highly of the team you had together. He lives in the next county, and it is probably easier for him to put together a team that can practice closer to his home. Why don't you reach out to Darren and congratulate him on the new team and see if you can help him in any way? Ask how everything is going with him, and then listen. It is more important to support him than to think he is doing anything to you. The new team probably has nothing to do with you. Also, ask him if we can pick up your water bottle after we drop Peter at home later today?"

Justin did not look happy, but he said, "Okay, Mom. You are probably right. We did not want Darren to leave. He is super-fast, and it is going to be hard to find someone to replace him. I did not even think about how far the drive is for him or what might be going on in his life. I will text him and congratulate him on the team and see if we can pick up my water bottle later today. Maybe we can get him a new water bottle as a gift. What do you think?"

Linda knew they had time to stop at the store on the way to drop off Peter later. She said, "Sure, I think that is a generous and kind idea. That way, Darren will know you support him."

As soon as Linda stopped speaking, her daughter Kim started talking. She said, "Mom, I need to get some supplies at the store when you go. I have to redo all my student council posters for the election."

"We just finished all those posters last week. Why do you have to redo them?" Linda said.

"Jessica Park decided to run for student council, too, and she used the same slogan I'm using. She stole my idea to say, 'I'm the one to get it done!' Now I need to think of a new slogan and redo all my signs."

Paul broke into the conversation. He said, "Do not worry if someone uses your idea. You were the first one to use it in this election, and people know the truth. Plus, Jessica may think it was her idea. Are you the only person to ever say, 'I'm the one to get it done?' Just leave your signs the way they are, and make sure to explain why you think your ideas for the student council are the best to help everyone in your grade and in the school. It will take care of itself. You just need to trust that the truth takes care of everything. It may be interesting if you both use the same slogan. You might be able to reach more people and accomplish more positive change together. Jessica may think she thought of the idea for the slogan first. You just never know."

Kim started to say something back, and then she stopped. She did not want to be a bad example in front of her younger brothers, and she was also remembering the message from church.

Just then, Douglas, Linda's middle child, started speaking. He said, "I need everyone's help. My friend Logan decided to leave our band and start his own band. I tried to be okay with this, even though I did not understand his reasons. However, Logan is calling his band the Shamrocks. We are all Irish, and our band is the Four-Leaf Clovers. It is so annoying. He is texting and messaging all our fans and telling them to go to see his band. I do not get why he must take our Irish theme and our fans. Should I go confront him and tell him to stop copying our name and stealing our fans?"

G·L·U·E

Linda looked at her husband. She was wondering if everyone was playing a joke on her. All the topics and examples were hitting too close to home.

She said to Douglas, "You should congratulate Logan on his new band. Let him go and grow his own audience and follow his own dream. Understanding that people wanting to grow and follow their own dream is a normal part of life. It is a great opportunity to support them. Sometimes people make good decisions with how they go about the growth process, and other times they do not. Our job is not to judge them. It is to let them go and let them grow. It is good friendship and good leadership to help other people grow. We grow in the process of supporting and helping others in their growth. Our job is to understand as best as possible and then extend love to them. It is our job to trust that it will all work out, be peacemakers and keep our relationships and families and communities strong instead of letting things split apart when people want to go and grow. Who knows, maybe you can join together and have a concert where you and other Irish bands draw the biggest crowd of fans yet."

As she was saying it, Linda knew that she needed to do the same thing with Cindy. She still did not think what Cindy was doing was right, but she knew that being angry would only continue to cause hurt to her own health and well-being. It was also not the right example for her family and community. Plus, she and Cindy had not even fully communicated about the situation. She was letting negativity fill the void where communication would help.

If Cindy was trying to leave with a copy of their client list, or if she was leaving with any intellectual property that belonged to The Hope Chest, then they would need to work that out in an ethical fashion. If Cindy wanted to go and grow toward her own dreams, then Linda did not have to agree, but she did need to follow the message from church. She needed to trust God. It was the right thing for her own peace and happiness and her family and her community. No one needed any more division and split relationships. There was too much threatening the unity, joy, and peace in the community right now anyway. There were so many areas of life where people gave in to anger instead of working through the challenge. Each time that occurred, people, families, and communities grew further apart. It weakened everyone.

She needed to do her part, no matter how small, to unite, not divide—to build, not destroy. She wanted to be a peacemaker. Her mother used to always say to her, "The first to make peace is the strongest," when she and her sisters would have arguments. Linda was starting to wonder the real reason why she got mad so quickly in the situation with Cindy. Linda had been a successful businesswoman and community leader for many years, and it was surprising to her that even seasoned and successful business professionals could get tripped up by situations like this. She knew her reaction was not mature. She was not acting like the friend, business leader, and community leader she had worked hard to be for so many years. The more she thought about it, she realized that a big piece of her reaction was due to lack of preparation. She had taken training in many things, but she had not prepared for something like this. She knew better than to jump to conclusions and let her negative emotions influence her actions in such a significant way. She continued to shift her mind and renew her focus on trust.

As she was thinking about how she would move forward the next day, Linda heard her husband say, "I think you are all sharing a valuable lesson with me." This surprised Linda. She thought the examples her family was sharing were God's way of shining some light on the opportunity to be more supportive and repair her relationship with Cindy. She spoke up and said, "What do you mean, Paul? I thought this lesson was for me."

Paul said, "In the last few weeks, two of my sales team told me they are moving on to new opportunities and leaving our company. One of them is doing it the right way. She shared why she is leaving and spoke with me about the decision and how the new opportunity is best for her. I am not sure I agree completely, but she shared her perspective, and I truly want the best for her and will always support her. She is behaving professionally about the transition. The other person's last day was on Friday, and he got caught copying his client list from our CRM (Customer Relationship Management) system. Both situations were not great because it would be easier right now if I did not have to make the extra time investment required to hire new people and communicate the change to the clients in those territories.

However, I needed to have a better attitude related to the idea of people leaving the team. I want to help people grow their careers and support their families the best way they can, not be selfish and force people to stay with me—or feel that our relationship is at risk if they grow into a new path. They need to be able to do what is best for themselves and make their own decisions. I would not be a good leader if I tried to hold them back, and I genuinely want them to be successful. I had bosses that did not support me in the past, and it was a horrible experience. I also had outstanding and supportive leadership, and it meant the world to me. I grew so much with their support, and I worked even harder knowing that they believed in me and truly wanted the best for me—not just for themselves. What is happening with my sales team made me think about this again and how I can be even better prepared as a leader for these situations in the future. I've already grown working through the current situations, and I will not respond the same way the next time this happens.

We all need to get ready for the situations where people leave us to go and grow. When they do, they usually take what they learned with them, and that is a good and natural process. It requires understanding and extending our love when people move to their next thing. Sometimes the person leaves in a professional and respectful way, and sometimes there are complications that require additional management. Regardless, we will best keep our own peace, our team peace, and our business and community peace by letting them go and grow, understanding the best we can, and extending love regardless of how they manage the process. We have an opportunity to show our leadership character in these situations.

Our job is to love above the way they act, so we can stay united and healthy and strong. That person may end up leaving and coming back. They may end up becoming a future client. They may end up partnering with us on a project. Or, they may come back and say they are sorry and learned a valuable lesson from leaving at the wrong time or in the wrong way. Regardless of what happens, the person can either become a life-long friend or a broken relationship by the way you handle the process. Whether it is a personal or a professional situation, our job is to be the G.L.U.E."

Linda said, "What do you mean, G.L.U.E.?"

"G.L.U.E. is something I thought of when I was watching Justin earlier while you all were setting the table and fixing the tacos."

While his dad was talking, Justin got up from the table and returned with Linda's business award and the mini replica of the

G·L·U·E

hope chest. Both were fixed. He put them down in front of his mom.

Justin said, "I used glue to put these back together because I know they mean a lot to you. Glue is for repairing things that are broken or split apart. It joins them back together and forms a new bond where there was a break. If you glue the items correctly, you can create an even stronger bond than before. I glued these when we got back from church because I was thinking about the importance of peace. You have always told us to be peacemakers and to be flexible and adaptable to be strong. I know it is important to you that we trust in God and His plan and His word. I wanted to bring peace back to you. Being a peacemaker brings contentment and joy, and you looked so troubled and did not smile the past two days. I hope this helps. You started The Hope Chest as a store to give joy and hope to others for important times in their life, and I wanted to restore joy and hope for you."

Linda looked at the two items. She looked at Justin, and she looked at Paul and all the other people at the table. She heard the words of the pastor from earlier in her head. *Trust in the Lord with all your heart. Lean not on your own understanding. In all your ways, acknowledge Him, and He will make your paths straight.* She was thinking of another thing that glue represented. It just popped into her mind. It felt like a divine revelation. She knew that G.L.U.E. stood for *God's Love Unites Everyone.* She realized G.L.U.E. is the true source of unity and strength.

She smiled. She was smiling because she felt the love in her heart again. It did not make sense because she still felt frustrated by the situation, but she knew she could get through it. She knew what to do.

Paul said, "I watched Justin gluing your things back together, and while I watched him, it popped into my mind. I knew the truth about applying G.L.U.E. G.L.U.E. stands for God's Love Unites Everyone. I also know how we can use it and apply it for stronger bonds in our friend, family, business, team, and community relationships when there are splits or breaks or just to make relationships stronger. I need to be ready to use G.L.U.E. at work, and I want my team to know they can count on that type of support and leadership."

Linda looked at Paul. She was stunned that Paul was spelling out the power of G.L.U.E. the exact way she just thought about it. They appeared to have had a divine revelation at the same time. He always amazed her with how he could take something seemingly complicated and make it simple. He knew how to coach people with instructions anyone could follow, and it was a powerful gift. Linda decided at that moment to take his coaching and apply G.L.U.E. to the situation with Cindy. Whatever happened, she would extend love. She would trust that it would all work out, and she would reclaim her own peace and the peace of her household. Everyone would be stronger and united.

Paul got up and came back with a pen and piece of paper. He wrote about G.L.U.E. and the way to apply it and showed it to everyone at the table.

He said, "I think we can all use this to help ourselves and others."

This is what Paul wrote:

G·L·U·E

> ### G.L.U.E.:
> ### *God's Love Unites Everyone.*
>
> How to apply G.L.U.E. in personal or
> work relationships:
>
> 1. Get ready. It is going to happen. It is
>   a part of life.
> 2. Let them go and let them grow.
> 3. Understand their vision as best you
>   can and believe the best of them.
> 4. Extend love even when it is hard. You
>   grow, too.

They all agreed that G.L.U.E. was the answer to the situations they were facing.

Each person smiled and got up from the table to start clearing the dishes.

Everyone knew what they would do next, especially Linda, but first, she had a call to make.

Chapter Nine

Follow the Leader

"You are blessed when you can show people how to cooperate instead of compete or fight. That's when you discover who you really are, and your place in God's family."

— Matthew 5:9, MSG

After the family finished the dishes and Linda drove Peter home, she headed back to her office. She was smiling again. She was smiling because they stopped by Darren's after they dropped off Peter. Justin got his water bottle back from Darren. He congratulated Darren on his new team and gave Darren the gift of a new water bottle. The boys had a wonderful conversation. Darren was so grateful for the support, and he said he was worried Justin and Peter were mad at him. Justin said they were not and wanted to support Darren with his new team. Darren got choked up and shared that his mom had told him he had to start his own team because she was not able to drive him so far for practice. He would not have been able to keep playing if he did not figure something out. He worried that it would cause a break in the relationships with his other team. Now he knew he could continue to look forward to getting better at football closer to home, so they could all come back together in high school and play their best in their high school years. Linda also made a mental note to reach out to Darren's mom and see if she could help her with anything. She did not want to let busyness get in the way of being supportive. She did not know her well, and it would be wonderful to make a new friend and support the boys' friendship.

Linda kept smiling because Douglas called to say he was putting together an event to include his friend's new band. While she was finishing the call with Douglas, Kim got on the phone to let her know that she was not going to change any of her campaign posters. She said, "I am going to let Jessica do her thing and trust that running on the issues will be enough for the election to work out the way it should."

Linda knew that Paul was probably working on solutions for how he would manage the two people leaving his sales team. They were all working on applying G.L.U.E. to repair and strengthen relationships while everyone grew stronger in the process. They were not distracted by making up stories about why people were leaving to do new things, and they were enjoying peace.

Linda's smile grew bigger because she was thinking about how great it felt to put the business award and the mini hope chest back on her shelf where they belonged. She was ready for the conversation with Cindy tomorrow and wanted to do one more thing before getting ready for bed.

Linda sat down behind her desk and dialed the number for her pastor. Pastor Fred picked up on the first ring. He said, "Hello Linda. How are you?"

Linda shared all that had been happening, and she said she wanted to pray together before seeing Cindy the next day.

Pastor Fred said, "I'm so glad you made the decision to trust God and let His love unite you and the people you care about. You are choosing to *love above* the hurts and perceived offenses, and I know this works. Of course, we can pray. I would also like to share a short story with you."

He told her that when he was just starting as a pastor, he was at a wonderful church, and God called him to a new church. He said that he did not make the decision lightly, and he prayed about it for weeks before he told anyone. Then he had private conversations with a small group of trusted leaders at the church. After weeks of praying and waiting to make sure he was making the decision God was calling him to make, he shared the news with the congregation. Some people were surprised but managed to trust him, be happy for him, support him, and wish him well. Others were frustrated and even angry with him. The angry people did not speak to him on his last Sunday and did not have kind words of encouragement for him and his wife as they left to the place God had called them. It still bothered him that those relationships were fractured at the end.

He said, "I am sharing this because these situations are a part of life. The only way to have peace is to trust God and leave all the consequences to Him. A pastor I admire, Pastor Charles Stanley, says this all the time in his messages, and when this happened to me, I repeated that phrase many times because my heart hurt when people were not happy for us and did not encourage us. However, the situation taught me how to get ready for when this might happen to me again in life. I knew that someone might have to leave my church or team, and I would have to be ready. I wanted to be ready to let them go and let them grow as God called them in their life. Sometimes people handle this process well, sometimes not, but they always need our love and support. I believe we should *love above* the feelings and hurt. In God's Word, there are many places we are called to provide understanding to others and to extend love even when it is hard. I meditate on 1 Corinthians 1:10 when these situations occur.

"'I appeal to you, brothers and sisters, in the name of our Lord Jesus Christ, that all of you agree with one another in what you say and that there be no divisions among you, but that you be perfectly united in mind and thought.' There are a couple of other verses that encourage me with the truth in these types of situations, and I will send those to you, too. Another thing I do in this type of challenging circumstance is read chapter 4 in Ephesians, and I recommend you read it tonight and again right before you meet with Cindy. The chapter is thirty-two verses and focused on unity. Now, let's pray."

Linda was stunned. Her whole body was tingling. She had pinpricks listening to Pastor Fred talk about G.L.U.E. He did not know the exact details of how she had decided to trust God for His help earlier in the day and her thoughts about the meaning of G.L.U.E. He did not know that her husband Paul shared what G.L.U.E. (God's Love Unites Everyone) meant just a few hours ago. He did not know that Paul had walked through the same steps he had just described on how to apply G.L.U.E. earlier in the evening. She was realizing G.L.U.E. existed way before she had a name for it.

Now, here they were, and Pastor Fred was saying the exact same things she and her family had been talking about. Moments of confirmation like this filled her with hope and strength. Her chest felt open and free again. She took a deep breath and inhaled the hope. She knew her hope was strong, and, thanks to her son Justin, the mini hope chest on the shelf was bonded together with new strength, too. Linda decided to share G.L.U.E. with Pastor Fred, so he could be encouraged by the process Paul explained to her and how it mirrored what Pastor Fred was already applying in his own life. She said, "Listen to what Paul said to me when our family was discussing our personal and work relationship challenges earlier today."

G.L.U.E.: *God's Love Unites Everyone.*

How to apply G.L.U.E. in personal or work relationships:

1. Get ready. It is going to happen. It is a part of life.
2. Let them go and let them grow.
3. Understand their vision as best you can and believe the best of them.
4. Extend love even when it is hard. You grow, too.

After Linda shared the G.L.U.E. process, they started to pray. She felt the power of the prayer. She felt her mind being renewed because she was focused on the truth. She was ready for the day tomorrow and the conversation with Cindy. She also began to consider that God's plan might be even better than what she originally planned for The Hope Chest and her relationship with Cindy. Maybe The Hope Chest and Cindy's store could bring three times the joy and celebration to the community. She was ready to find out, and she believed it was possible.

She knew all it would take was G.L.U.E., and she knew how to apply it.

Author's Pause

Before you read the conversation between Cindy and Linda, please take a minute to pause and reflect on the challenging life and work conversations you might have had in your life. Think about conversations where one person may have decided to leave a relationship, team, or organization to go and grow in a new direction. Or a time you might have thought someone took one of your ideas and claimed it as their own. These conversations come in many forms. Sometimes the conversations are heated and contentious. Some take hours over multiple days with many highs and lows. Some of these conversations cause seemingly permanent breaks in family and work relationships. These conversations can be emotional and life-changing. As you think about the past, consider situations that might be on the horizon and how you can prepare for success. The more you can appreciate the mindsets of the characters, the more you can build the ability to examine multiple sides of a challenging situation and be ready with the power of G.L.U.E.

With preparation, you will be ready to apply it for your own benefit and the benefit of others in the leadership story of your life. G.L.U.E. is for stronger bonds and unity.

Chapter Ten

G.L.U.E. Helps Everyone Grow

"For he himself is our peace, who has made the two groups one and has destroyed the barrier, the dividing wall of hostility."

— Ephesians 2:14

Linda and Cindy had a difficult conversation the next day. At the beginning of the conversation, their relationship showed signs of division and brokenness. As they listened to each other, they realized the division went back a few years and started with poor communication and a lack of belief in the other person's positive motivations. In some ways, it felt like they were listening to each other for the first time.

The conversation was one the women should have had years ago. Some people call these hard conversations, but Linda and Cindy decided to call their talk a *heart conversation* because they shared what was on their heart from a place of trust and positive belief in the other person. They reserved judgment and did not try to interpret the other woman's motive. The *heart conversation* revealed things the business partners and friends should have communicated from the start and would have made a big difference in both their perspectives for their business partnership and friendship. They never clarified the roles that each would play in their business, and they never had regular meetings. They also realized that they focused most of their time in a reactionary mode solving problems and discussing what was not working without making sure to encourage each other and point out the things that each was doing well. They stopped talking about their hopes and dreams and how this related to their shared vision and greater purpose with The Hope Chest. They also stopped truly listening to each other and thinking of the other's needs as much as they did their own. This was one of the reasons Linda missed Cindy's cues related to the importance of jewelry as one of her major interests in the business.

They were grateful to address these issues now and felt a little silly for having let small things create a fracture in the relationship. However, because of G.L.U.E., this fracture would heal. They knew they could restore their relationship. They wanted to be one, big, happy family again without any walls between them.

Cindy shared that she sometimes felt Linda did not appreciate her contribution to the business and did not listen to her input. She thought Linda diminished her tasks and acted like her own contribution was more important and valuable. Cindy said she felt like Linda got to have all the fun with the customers while selling products and building relationships, and Cindy would have to make sure they had enough inventory, payroll was paid, and they could pay bills on time.

Cindy started feeling this way years ago. She never said anything because she thought Linda would figure it out and start appreciating her or see how it was impacting her and ask what was wrong. The more time passed, the more resentment built, and the distance between the partners grew. The women started to view everything through the lens of resentment, and it clouded even the positive interactions with that perspective. Cindy began to think Linda was selfish and did not pull her weight in the administrative tasks to keep the business running. Cindy started keeping track of all she did, and when she compared it to what she thought Linda contributed, it did not seem fair. She started to believe that what Linda did was insignificant, and she knew that was not true. As the resentment continued to build, she started considering new plans for the future. Eventually, Cindy did not imagine Linda in her future plans. Without communicating through regular discussion and listening, they ended up here.

Linda never realized Cindy felt this way. Linda thought Cindy appreciated her ability to come up with new ideas and keep the excitement and energy flowing for the store while sharing gift ideas and new products with the customers. Linda thought Cindy could have done a better job of being supportive, appreciative, and excited about new products and promoting sales and events for the store. She admitted that there were many times she thought Cindy hid behind her paperwork because she did not want to expend the energy to do the hard work of developing relationships and contacting potential and existing customers. Linda also did not like that Cindy would purchase supplies and inventory without getting her input. Linda said that she thought Cindy liked being involved in the paperwork because it was easier to do those tasks any time of day and any place. Linda always had to be in the store and ready for the ups and downs of the busy and slow days.

Over the years, there were quite a few times Cindy bought equipment and store decorations without any input from her business partner. When Linda shared her frustration with Cindy, it revealed that Cindy thought she was helping Linda by not having to worry about those tasks. Linda thought it was presumptuous to spend the business partners' money without some collaboration or agreement. Each woman had a list of things that had been on their minds, but neither had made the steps to broach specific communication. It was obvious to the women that they had started to look at the other with the eyes of a critic and not the eyes of someone that believed the best and wanted the best for the other person.

They were both surprised to hear the other person's perspective during the *heart conversation*, but they were grateful to see the pattern that emerged in their thinking. Many things that were said still stung a little, and Linda had to continuously remind herself about G.L.U.E. to stay calm and in the most receptive state of mind. As the conversation continued, they realized much of the issue was a misunderstanding that started by not communicating. When communication did not occur, each woman made up their own story for the motives of the other. They both allowed their lack of communication to lead to frustration and misunderstanding. They also realized that if they were honest, they had both been placing a higher value on their own contribution to the business and not looking as closely at the effort and contribution of the other. They realized their leadership had suffered because leaders think about how to serve others, not just worry about themself.

This was an important realization for both women because they knew it revealed a root of pride that is easy for anyone to succumb to in life and work. They thought they did the most work and the most important work, and they had started thinking, *What about me? Why doesn't everyone appreciate me for all the work I am doing?* They noticed that when their frustration grew, eventually, they focused primarily on themselves and started to get bitter. They lost the joy in their work and relationship. The *heart conversation* allowed them to tell each other the truth in a loving way, and it made them both truly sorry and want to genuinely apologize.

Cindy apologized to Linda for surprising her with her seemingly abrupt desire to start her own store. Linda apologized to Cindy for not being more focused on appreciating all she had added to the business's success over the years. They both shared what was on their heart, listened, and took action to apologize. The conversation made a huge difference, and the fact that Linda prepared by focusing on G.L.U.E. was the foundational factor in the conversation's success.

The *heart conversation* provided an environment where they were both able to believe the best about each other again. Linda applied G.L.U.E. successfully as they spoke through the various topics that both women needed to share.

Linda listened to Cindy and her vision for her store. Much of what Linda had been thinking about Cindy's plans was not accurate. Cindy truly wanted Linda's support and to honor all the work they had done together over the years. She wanted to help with a successful transition. Cindy was just ready to grow more toward her dreams. She needed to try something on her own, and she wanted Linda's support. Linda told Cindy she wanted her to be successful in her dreams, even though it was hard to let her go and grow a new store. They had to communicate to work through the misunderstanding. They had to heal the hurt, apply G.L.U.E. to repair the break, and form a stronger bond.

G·L·U·E

Linda shared the lesson about G.L.U.E. with Cindy, and the two women continued to have regular *heart conversations* and prayer time, together and separately, in the months that followed. Their bond grew stronger, and they were more united than ever. They also came up with their most creative and innovative business ideas yet because they listened to each other and prioritized what was important to the other.

They maintained their communication and connection. The communication and connection kept their commitment to each other strong, and they were able to continue to show each other how much they cared. They even gave each other gifts from their stores and sometimes left post-it notes of encouragement on the door to each other's businesses.

It was not easy during those months. It took work, and they had to make the choice every day to share a sustained commitment to communicate and protect their bond. Each woman had to grow, understand, and extend love many times. In the end, the two women grew as friends, parents, and business professionals. Their relationship was a source of inspiration to many in the community and would become a life-long friendship. They were both grateful they used G.L.U.E. and did not let a break become a painful and bitter thing in their lives and community. They shared G.L.U.E. with as many people as possible, and they started a product line based on G.L.U.E. that was a best-seller in both stores. Both women wore a necklace with a tiny gold glue bottle as a symbol of their bond.

A few years later, Cindy called Linda to let her know that her daughter Sarah wanted to leave her work at Cindy's store to start her own business. They both smiled and sent up a prayer of thanksgiving for the strong bond that united them and would help them as they supported Sarah while she grew. They knew

AMY P. KELLY

they would continue to be the leaders of their lives and help Sarah do the same through G.L.U.E.

"No one has ever seen God; but if we love one another, God lives in us, and his love is made complete in us."

— 1 John 4:12

Author's Final Notes on G.L.U.E.

"You will keep in perfect and constant peace the
one whose mind is steadfast [that is, committed and
focused on You—in both inclination and character],
Because he trusts and takes refuge in You [with
hope and confident expectation]."

— Isaiah 26:3 (AMP)

In life and work, I have seen people leave companies, neighborhoods, teams, and families. I have left teams and companies and joined news ones. I have had people leave my team and go to new organizations. I have had great relationships end. I have had family and work relationships break and heal, and some are still broken and waiting for G.L.U.E. to rebuild the bond. Sometimes, I was a positive contributor to the transition, and sometimes I was not.

Some of the people I have seen leave companies have done it professionally and some of the people have burned bridges and made mistakes. I've seen million-dollar deals moved to another company because of a broken business relationship. Being in the human resources and talent development profession and owning my own business provided the opportunity to observe transitions in and out of organizations and relationships many times. I have also had the experience myself in my personal and professional life, as well as in my church life. A great deal of valuable learning and growth has occurred.

Most of us have been on both sides of G.L.U.E. situations. It is a normal part of life. You might be leaving a job for a new company, or you might be freezing out a family member. You might be the person that does not understand why someone would want to leave your team. And you might question their motives and timing. It is not easy for any of the parties involved, and there can be many layers of issues that need to be addressed. Some situations take more time for the G.L.U.E. to form a new bond. Do not give up!

What I have seen is that the people who use G.L.U.E. keep relationships, families, businesses, and communities together. They know what to do to apply G.L.U.E. to build or rebuild a bond after a relationship is broken and splintered apart. They are peacemakers. They want peace for themselves and others, and they believe that peace is the type of environment for healthy growth. They lead with love in the leadership journey of their life.

G.L.U.E. is the greatest asset to unity that exists. It is the leadership development strategy to bond and unite. It is a central element to leading families, teams, and organizations. It is the single most powerful resource to heal the world, one relationship at a time.

It seems like every generation needs G.L.U.E. more and more, and we need to teach each other how to apply G.L.U.E. to stay unified, live joy-filled, productive lives, and set a good example for the next generation. It will not always look the same, and it will not always work as fast as we might like. It may not appear to even work at all, but we know the truth. When we are leading from a place of peace, that produces internal peace.

You are free and whole when you use G.L.U.E. to make peace and rebuild things that are broken in moments of anger, fear, and doubt. When you apply G.L.U.E., you are bonding and building and rebuilding and keeping things together for a much greater and eternal purpose. The results are amazing and far-reaching. You may never know all the positive outcomes that result from saving or repairing one broken relationship or letting one person go and grow with all your love and support. You grow when they grow.

The people in your home, business, and community are watching.

Choose to use G.L.U.E. Choose to be G.L.U.E.

You will see.

You will grow and build beautiful things through the process.

God's Love Unites Everyone!

"May the God of hope fill you with all joy and peace as you trust in him, so that you may overflow with hope by the power of the Holy Spirit."

— Romans 15:13

G·L·U·E

About the Author

Amy P. Kelly believes in people and works with individuals, teams, and organizations to help them grow. She loves business, teamwork, and the people that make it all happen. Amy is a human resources and learning and development executive who builds award-winning employment brands, world-class corporate universities, and transformational leadership development programs. She is an executive coach and consultant who manages and guides change initiatives and performance consulting projects while improving individual and organizational results. Amy has been married to Jim Kelly for over twenty years and is mom to Patrick, Natalie, Daniel, and Samuel. You can learn more about Amy by visiting www.amypkelly.com.

"Make every effort to keep the unity of the Spirit through the bond of peace."

— Ephesians 4:3

G.L.U.E.

God's Love Unites Everyone

How to apply G.L.U.E. in personal or work relationships:

1. Get ready. It is going to happen. It is a part of life.
2. Let them go and let them grow.
3. Understand their vision as best you can and believe the best of them.
4. Extend love even when it is hard. You grow, too.

CPSIA information can be obtained
at www.ICGtesting.com
Printed in the USA
LVHW052119210122
708928LV00011B/472

9 781637 697